D1170778

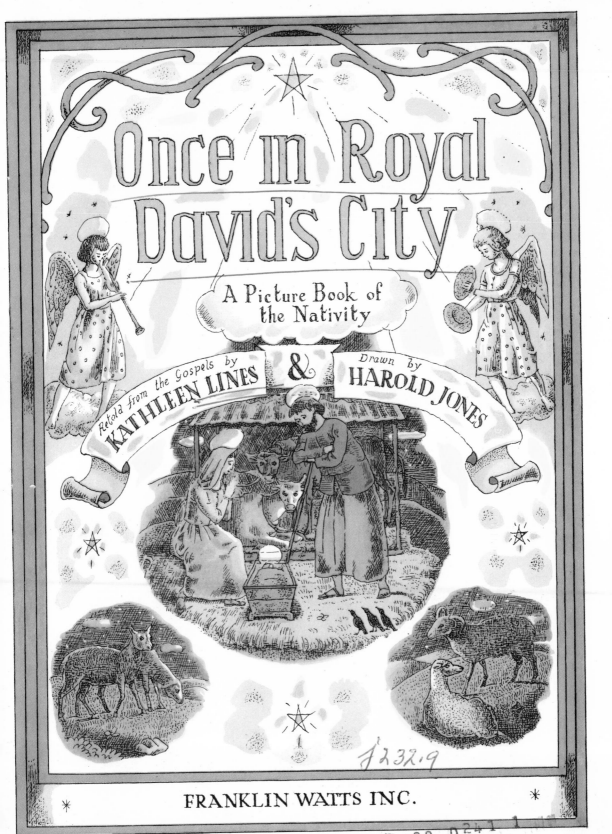

Once in Royal David's City

A Picture Book of the Nativity

Retold from the Gospels by **KATHLEEN LINES** & *Drawn by* **HAROLD JONES**

FRANKLIN WATTS, INCORPORATED
699 Madison Avenue
New York 21, N.Y.

First published 1956

PRINTED IN GREAT BRITAIN BY
MORRISON AND GIBB LTD., LONDON AND EDINBURGH

In the days of Herod king of Judaea the angel Gabriel was sent from God to a city of Galilee named Nazareth

To a maiden whose name was Mary

Mary was to marry Joseph
of the house and family of David

The angel said
Thou shalt have a son   Thou shalt call his name Jesus

Behold the handmaid of the Lord

At this time the Emperor in Rome ordered every
man to go to his family city to be taxed

Joseph took Mary up into Judaea to Bethlehem the
city of David

And because there was no room for them in the inn

Mary's little son was born in the stable

Once in royal David's city
Stood a lowly cattle shed
Where a mother laid her baby

In a manger for his bed :
Mary was that mother mild
Jesus Christ her little child

While shepherds watched over their flocks by night

the angel of the Lord appeared to them saying

I bring tidings of great joy to you and to all people
for there is born this day in the city of David

a Saviour which is Christ the Lord
You shall find the babe lying in a manger

And there was a multitude

of the heavenly host praising God

Then the shepherds came with haste to the stable and found

Mary and Joseph and the babe lying in a manger

Away in the east wise men saw a new star They came to He

asking Where is the new born king ? We are come to worship him

Herod said Go to Bethlehem search diligently for the young

child and when you have found him bring me word

But the star appeared again and led the wise men

to the place where the young child was

They fell down and worshipped him and when they had

opened their treasure they presented him with gifts

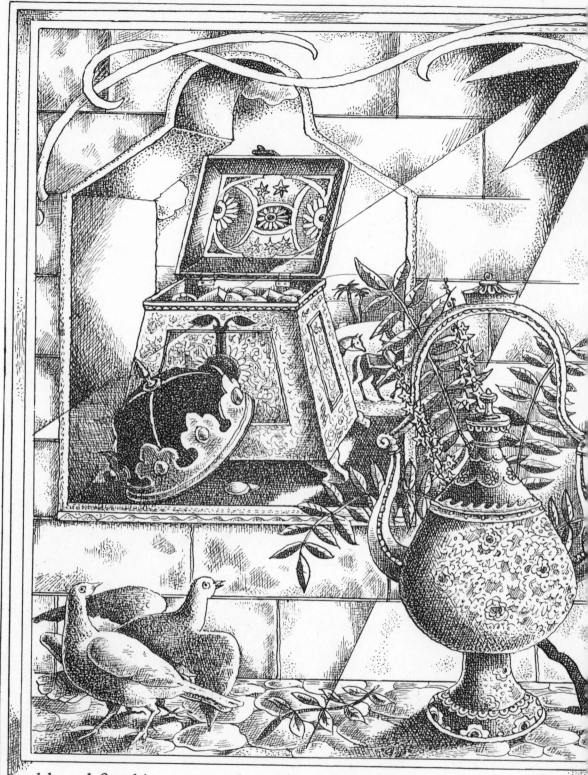

gold and frankincense and myrrh in homage to the little child wh

GOLD AND FRANKINCENSE AND MYRRH

...vas Jesus Christ the Lord, the King they had come so far to seek

God warned the wise men not to go back to Herod

so they departed into their own country another way

Then the angel of the Lord appeared unto Joseph
in a dream and said

Herod will seek the young child to destroy him
Arise and flee into Egypt

They went away.

secretly in the night

When the wise men did not come to tell him
where they had found the infant Jesus

Herod was filled with wrath   He sent his soldiers
to kill all the young children of Bethlehem

After two years had passed and Herod was dead
God called Joseph out of Egypt

Joseph and Mary and the child Jesus
came back to their own city of Nazareth

The child grew and waxed strong in spirit

and the grace of God was upon him

The Birth of Jesus from the Gospels according to St Luke and St Matthew

In the days of Herod the king of Judaea, the angel Gabriel was sent from God to a city of Galilee, named Nazareth, to a virgin espoused to a man whose name was Joseph, of the house of David; and the virgin's name was Mary. And the angel came in unto her, and said,

> Hail, thou that art highly favoured, the Lord is with thee: blessed art thou among women.

And when she saw him, she was troubled at his saying, and cast in her mind what manner of salutation this should be. And the angel said unto her,

> Fear not, Mary: for thou hast found favour with God. And thou shalt conceive and bring forth a son, and shalt call his name JESUS. He shall be great, and shall be called the Son of the Highest: and the Lord God shall give unto him the throne of his father David: and he shall reign over the house of Jacob for ever; and of his kingdom there shall be no end.

And Mary said,

> Behold the handmaid of the Lord; be it unto me according to thy word.

And it came to pass in those days, that there went out a decree from Caesar Augustus that all the world should be taxed. And all went to be taxed, everyone into his own city. And Joseph also went up from Galilee, out of the city of Nazareth, into Judaea, unto the city of David, which is called Bethlehem—because he was of the house and lineage of David —to be taxed with Mary his espoused wife, being great with child. And so it was that, while they were there, the days were accomplished that she should be delivered. And she brought forth her firstborn son, and wrapped him in swaddling clothes, and laid him in a manger; because there was no room for them in the inn.

And there were in the same country shepherds abiding in the field, keeping watch over their flock by night. And lo, the angel of the Lord came unto them, and the glory of the Lord shone round them: and they were sore afraid. And the angel said unto them,

> Fear not: for behold, I bring you good tidings of great joy, which shall be to all people. For unto you is born this day in the city of David a Saviour, which is Christ the Lord. And this shall be a sign unto you; Ye shall find the babe wrapped in swaddling clothes, lying in a manger.

And suddenly there was with the angel a multitude of the heavenly host praising God, and saying,

Glory to God in the highest, and on earth
peace, good will towards men.

And it came to pass, as the angels were gone away from them into heaven, the shepherds said one to another, Let us now go even unto Bethlehem, and see this thing which is come to pass, which the Lord hath made known unto us. And they came with haste, and found Mary, and Joseph, and the babe lying in a manger.

And the shepherds returned, glorifying and praising God for all the things they had heard and seen.

Now there came wise men from the east to Jerusalem, saying, Where is he that is born King of the Jews? For we have seen his star in the east, and are come to worship him.

When Herod the king heard these things he was troubled. He called the chief priests and the scribes together and demanded of them where Christ should be born. And they told him in Bethlehem of Judaea. Then Herod sent the wise men to Bethlehem, and said, Go and search diligently for the young child; and when ye have found him, bring me word again, that I may come and worship him also.

When they had heard the king, they departed; and lo, the star which they saw in the east, went before them, till it came and stood over where the young child was.

And when they were come into the house, they saw the young child with Mary his mother, and fell down and worshipped him: and when they had opened their treasures, they presented unto him gifts; gold, frankincense, and myrrh.

And being warned of God in a dream that they should not return to Herod, they departed into their own country another way.

And behold, the angel of the Lord appeared to Joseph in a dream, saying, Arise, and take the young child and his mother, and flee into Egypt, and be thou there until I bring thee word: for Herod will seek the young child to destroy him. When he arose, he took the young child and his mother by night, and departed into Egypt.

Then Herod, when he saw that he was mocked of the wise men, was exceeding wroth, and sent forth and slew all the children, from two years and under, that were in Bethlehem and in all the coasts thereof.

When Herod was dead, the angel of the Lord appeareth in a dream to Joseph in Egypt, saying, Arise, and take the young child and his mother, and go into the land of Israel: for they are dead which sought the young child's life.

And then he arose and took the young child and his mother, and came into the land of Israel, and they returned into Galilee to their own city Nazareth.

And the child grew, and waxed strong in spirit, filled with wisdom: and the grace of God was upon him.